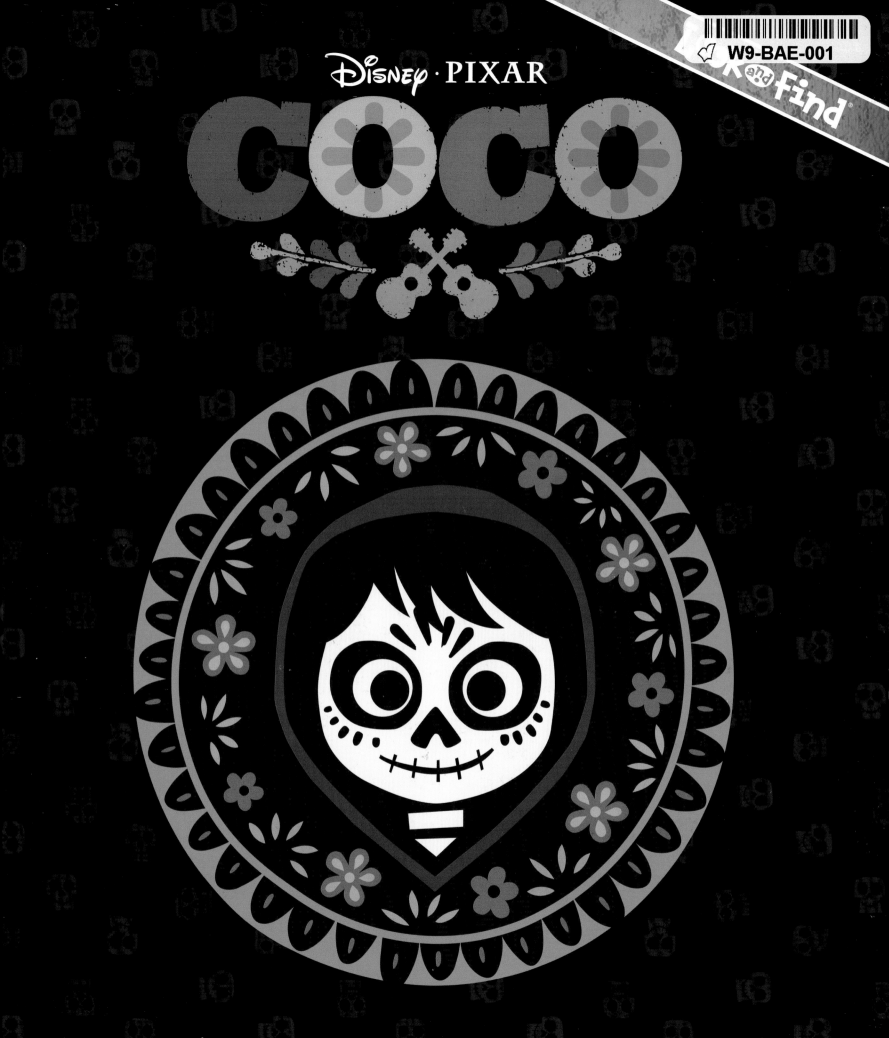

DISNEY · PIXAR

COCO

pi kids

Phoenix International Publications, Inc.

Chicago · London · New York · Hamburg · Mexico City · Paris · Sydney

In Santa Cecilia, young Miguel Rivera dreams of being a musician, though his family would never allow it. Long ago, Miguel's great-great-grandfather left with his guitar...and never came back. When Miguel wants to enter this year's Día de los Muertos talent show, Abuelita shouts, "No music!"

As Miguel's plans fizzle out, look for his family members and musical inspiration:

Prima Rosa

Dante

Miguel

statue of
Ernesto de la Cruz

Abuelita

Tío Berto

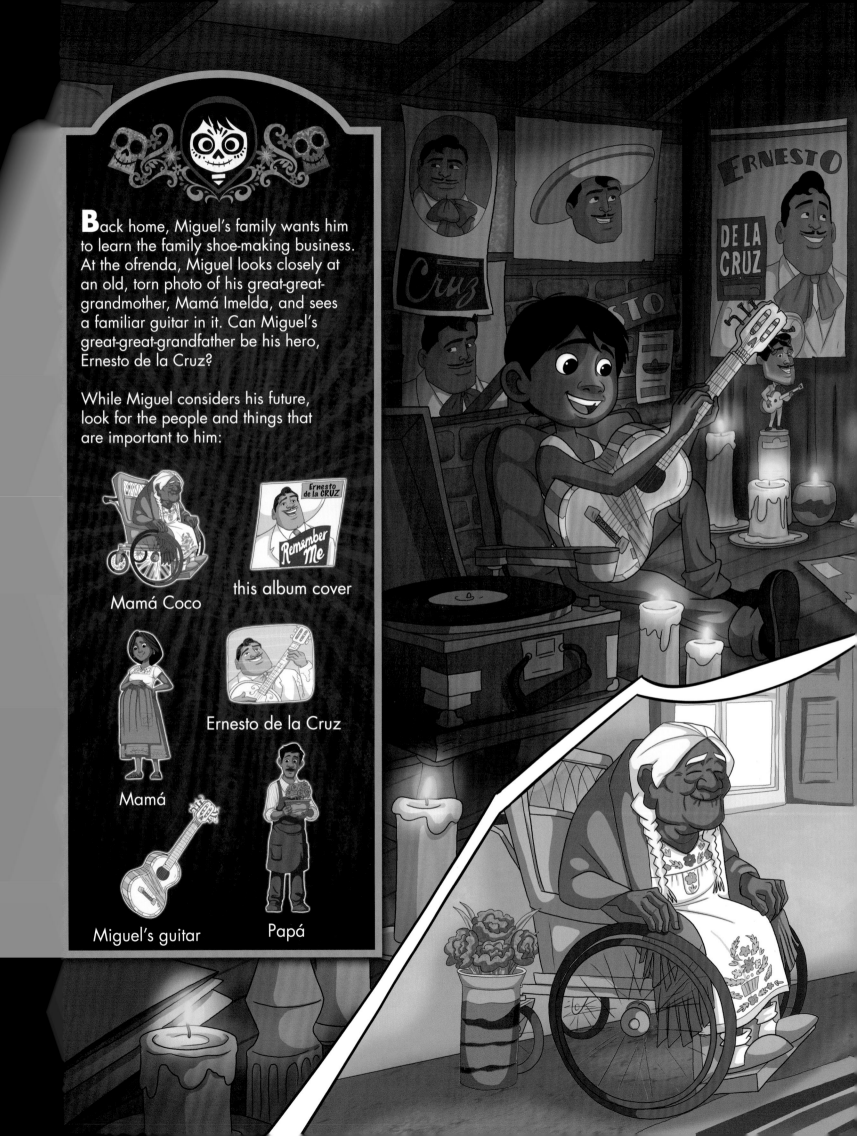

Back home, Miguel's family wants him to learn the family shoe-making business. At the ofrenda, Miguel looks closely at an old, torn photo of his great-great-grandmother, Mamá Imelda, and sees a familiar guitar in it. Can Miguel's great-great-grandfather be his hero, Ernesto de la Cruz?

While Miguel considers his future, look for the people and things that are important to him:

Mamá Coco

this album cover

Mamá

Ernesto de la Cruz

Miguel's guitar

Papá

Miguel decides to enter the talent show despite his family's wishes. But first he needs a working guitar, and he knows where to get one. At the cemetery, he talks himself into "borrowing" his great-great-grandfather's guitar. "You would've told me to follow my heart," says Miguel. "To seize my moment!"

While Día de los Muertos celebrations continue, help Miguel and these other villagers find what they're looking for:

the guitar in the photo

this villager

groundskeeper

this villager

this villager

Ernesto's guitar

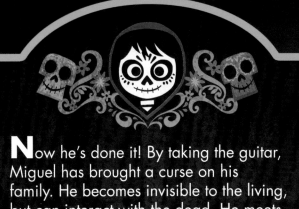

Now he's done it! By taking the guitar, Miguel has brought a curse on his family. He becomes invisible to the living, but can interact with the dead. He meets his deceased relatives on their way to the family ofrenda, and they offer to help him. Together, they cross over the Marigold Bridge into the Land of the Dead.

Look for these long-gone relatives as they try to figure out how to get Miguel back to the Land of the Living:

Tía Rosita

Tío Felipe

Papá Julio

Tío Óscar

Tía Victoria

little girl

Miguel learns he can return to the Land of the Living if he gets a blessing from a family member—before sunrise. When he runs into his Mamá Imelda, she agrees, with one condition...*that he never play music again.* "I need a musician's blessing," says Miguel. "We gotta find my great-great-grandpa." Miguel flees his family and finds Hector, who is willing to help.

While Miguel runs, search the Land of the Dead for these characters:

this security guard

this caseworker

Mamá Imelda

Hector

Dante

this bystander

Hector convinces Miguel to enter the Battle of the Bands. If Miguel wins, he'll be invited to Ernesto de la Cruz's huge Día de los Muertos party, where he can ask for Ernesto's blessing. They borrow a guitar, and Miguel performs for the first time! But his family is too close. He runs off to find Ernesto on his own.

Search the Battle of the Bands for Miguel, Hector, and these other performers:

dog orchestra

Hector

Dante

Miguel

nuns with accordions

this performer

Miguel crashes Ernesto's party. Then Hector barges in to reveal that Ernesto stole his songs. Miguel realizes that Hector is his true great-great-grandfather! Imelda finds Miguel and also learns the truth. Just before sunrise, she takes the stage with Ernesto and exposes him as a fraud. With Hector by her side once more, Imelda gives Miguel her blessing, with one condition... *"to never forget how much your family loves you."*

As the sun rises and the truth is revealed, find these characters backstage:

this bouncer

Hector

Dante as a spirit guide

Pepita

Tía Rosita

Ernesto de la Cruz

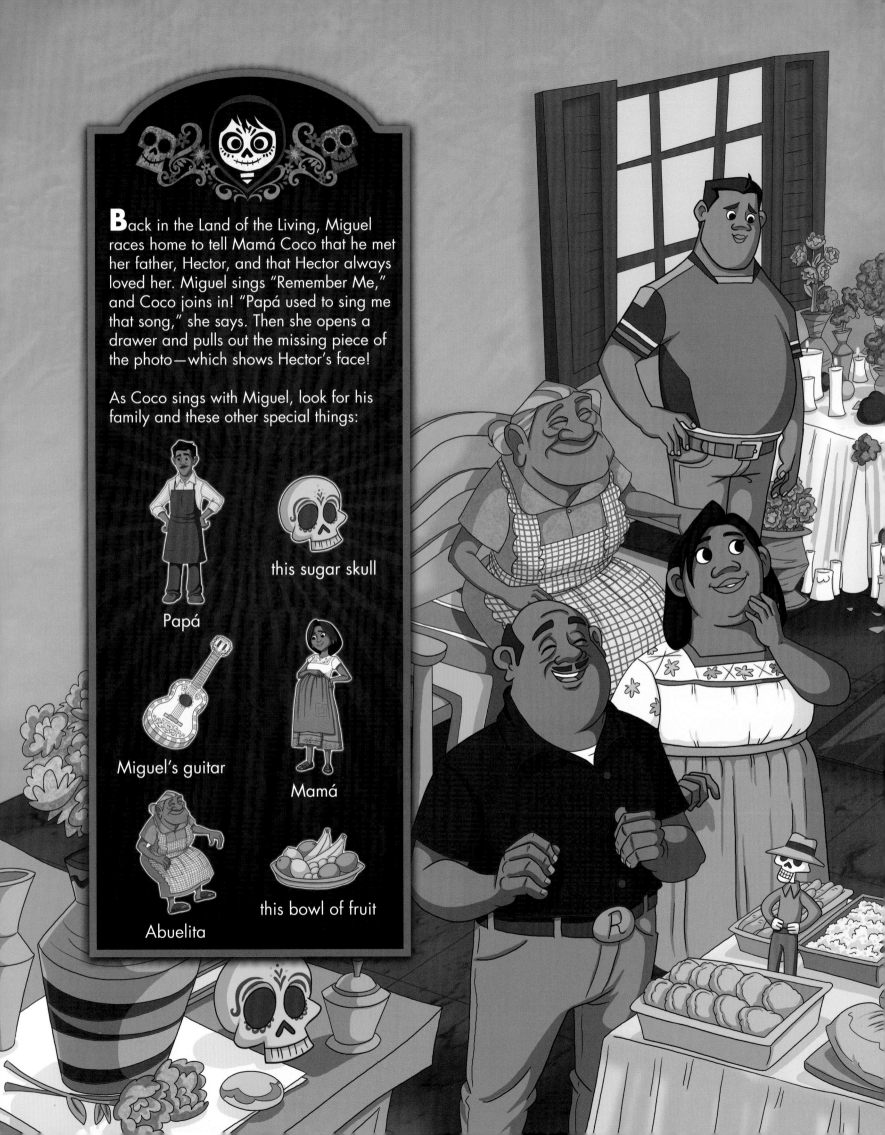

Back in the Land of the Living, Miguel races home to tell Mamá Coco that he met her father, Hector, and that Hector always loved her. Miguel sings "Remember Me," and Coco joins in! "Papá used to sing me that song," she says. Then she opens a drawer and pulls out the missing piece of the photo—which shows Hector's face!

As Coco sings with Miguel, look for his family and these other special things:

Papá

this sugar skull

Miguel's guitar

Mamá

Abuelita

this bowl of fruit

Run back to the plaza and find these things for the Día de los Muertos celebrations:

this guitar

talent show poster

this papel picado

these marigolds

this sugar skull

this pan dulce

Return to the two ofrendas and find these things that honor loved ones who have passed on:

this candle

this de la Cruz photo

this bread

this family photo

these flowers

torn photo

Creep back to the cemetery and find these gravestones:

REYES

GARCIA

LOPEZ

DIAZ

PEREZ

GONZALEZ

Cross back over the bridge and find these skeletons going to visit their families:

Go back to the Land of the Dead and find these spirit guides who look like colorful alebrijes:

Hurry back to the Battle of the Bands and find these musical instruments:

saxophone

drums

violin

trumpet

acoustic guitar

clarinet

Hurry back to the Sunrise Spectacular, and search for these unhappy fans:

Go back to Miguel's house and look for these items on the family ofrenda:

fancy boot

this basket of food

this bottle

this candle

this papier-mâché skeleton

these flowers

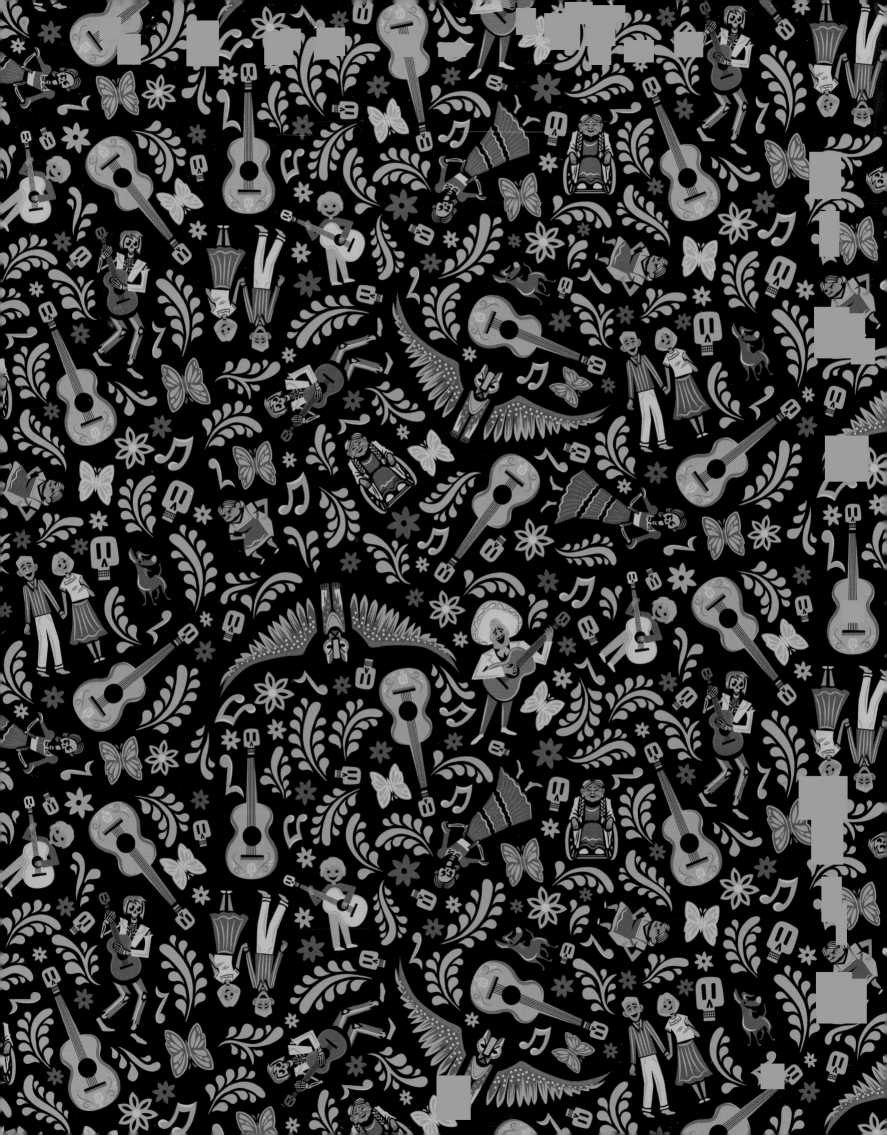